CW00864232

THE STRANGE TALES OF THE ALPHABET CHILDREN

In memory of my long-suffering and wonderful parents Neville and Frances Rumbelow, who did so much to nurture and encourage my love of English.

By Matthew Rumbelow

PREFACE

Most children's books don't need a preface. The subject matter is usually self-explanatory and the genre instantly recognisable. If you are browsing the children's fiction shelves and pick up *Geoffrey the Worried Elephant* or *I Love You Little Bear*, you know pretty much what you are getting. Chances are, it will be a picture book filled with fluffy animals and a few clumsy, well-meaning life lessons about building confidence and being kind to others.

The Strange Tales of the Alphabet Children is slightly different, hence the gnawing feeling that I really should give my readers some sort of prior warning. For while this book does occasionally impart some form of moralistic wisdom, there are no talking creatures, affable giants or friendly wizards.

Inspired by Hilaire Belloc's *Cautionary Tales for Children* and Edward Gorey's *Gashlycrumb Tinies*, the tales you are about to read are often gruesome, and peppered with words that even the brightest four-year-old is unlikely to know. Which is a long-winded way of saying that this is *not* a picture book for young children, unless you want them to be mildly traumatised.

For those unfamiliar with the *Gashlycrumb Tinies*, it is a slim ABC or abecedarian, each letter of the alphabet describing the sad demise of twenty-six children, beginning with Amy who fell down the stairs, and ending with Zillah, who drank too much gin. Each couplet is accompanied by a sinister pen and ink drawing showing the unfortunate child's final moments before disaster struck, but *how* they ended up in such a dire predicament is left to the reader's imagination.

I had just finished reciting the *Gashlycrumb Tinies* to a friend's wide-eyed seven year old, when it occurred to me that I could write my own backstory for each child. I decided to use rhyming verse to create a series of modern-day cautionary tales redolent of Belloc, while basing them around the structure of Gorey's abecedarian. *The Strange Tales of the Alphabet Children* was written as my homage to Gorey and Belloc, and their glorious brand of macabre, Gothic humour.

However, as anyone who knows the *Gashlycrumb Tinies* intimately will note, many of my tales do not match the original *modus operandi* of each child's tragic end. Hector, for example, is not strangled, Kate is not murdered in a snowy forest, and Prue is not trampled (presumably to death) in a saloon bar. Some children do not die at all, but escape to learn a salutary lesson. This was deliberate, for while I wanted to write a pastiche of the works that had inspired me, I also wanted to introduce themes that would be relevant and recognisable for a 21st century audience. This sometimes involved changing the location and circumstances of each story.

From that first seed of an idea, writing progressed quickly, and with the first draft completed early in 2018, I turned my attention to publishing and the daunting task of finding an agent. As many aspiring authors know, 'getting published' is far from straightforward. For me, I suspect the process was made harder not only by the dark, atypical subject matter and rhyming couplet style, but also because I struggled to identify an age category my book would comfortably fit into.

When I started writing, I naively assumed that I was creating a series of children's stories. But as my writing continued (and more and more children died in increasingly unpleasant and intricately described ways), I realised that these were not really children's stories at all. Stories *about* children, yes, but written *for* children? Well, perhaps not. I suspect that only time will tell whether this book comes to rest in a pigeonhole like 'Middle Grade' or 'Young Adult', or perhaps it will eternally float in literary no man's land, if it comes to rest at all.

Determined that the project would be completed one way or another, I busied myself with finding an illustrator. After a series of lengthy and ultimately fruitless discussions with one well-known artist, some talented friends and friends of friends generously donated sample illustrations to get the creative ball rolling. Then, in 2019, I was introduced to Deborah Panesar, whose pencil and digital wash illustrations felt like a perfect fit. I'm not sure either of us anticipated quite what a marathon task illustrating 26 stories would be, but Deborah pulled out all the stops and finished them in record time.

Editing, tweaking and rewriting continued. I recorded some audiobook versions, updated my website and social media pages, and prepared the manuscript for printing. Which brings us to where I am today, still tinkering with this preface as I debate how many copies I should order and whether to have a dust jacket.

All that remains is to thank you for buying this book. I also hope that you now have a brief insight into how *The Strange Tales of the Alphabet Children* came to be, and why the stories you are about to read describe such edifying subjects as suffocation, poisoning, mauling and road traffic accidents.

Matthew Rumbelow
December 2020

First published December 2020.

This first edition published through Rumbers Media.
Printed and bound in England by ExWhyZed Limited.
ISBN 978-1-5272-7854-7

Illustrated by Deborah Panesar. https://deborahpanesar.com

Typeset by me, because I'm reasonably handy with Adobe InDesign®. If you find any mistakes, please don't tell me. Or if you do, break it to me gently.

www.thealphabetchildren.co.uk

CONTENTS

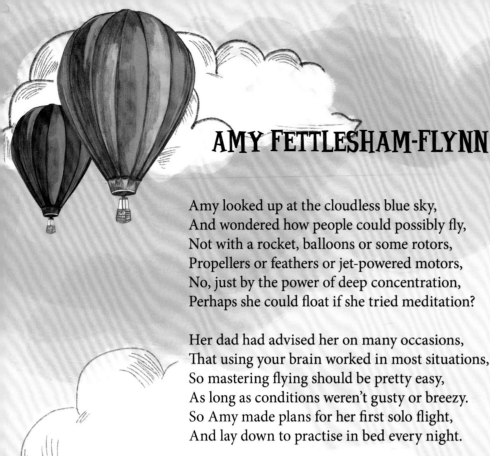

AMY FETTLESHAM-FLYNN

Amy looked up at the cloudless blue sky,
And wondered how people could possibly fly,
Not with a rocket, balloons or some rotors,
Propellers or feathers or jet-powered motors,
No, just by the power of deep concentration,
Perhaps she could float if she tried meditation?

Her dad had advised her on many occasions,
That using your brain worked in most situations,
So mastering flying should be pretty easy,
As long as conditions weren't gusty or breezy.
So Amy made plans for her first solo flight,
And lay down to practise in bed every night.

She'd close her eyes tight and imagine light things,
Like dust, or some bubbles, or butterfly wings.
Ignoring the fact of the ground underneath her,
She tried levitation by one millimetre.
But stuck she remained, firmly fixed on the ground,
This mind over matter was hard, Amy frowned.

She opened her eyes both dismayed and frustrated,
For willpower clearly was quite overrated!
Perhaps what she needed was not thought alone,
But ramps or a launch pad or some sort of drone
To give her some height that would help her to glide.
"Eureka!" she shouted, "I've got it!", she cried.

The easiest way to become elevated,
Was climbing the stairs that her parents had gated
To stop little children from climbing too high,
But Amy ascended, determined to fly.
She took out some pliers and prised up the latch,
Tonight she would try out the plan she had hatched.

Her brother reported he'd witnessed her standing
With arms held out wide at the top of the landing.
She stood there awhile with her eyes looking up,
Reciting a mantra she'd just conjured up.
Then Amy leapt off with a triumphant jump
And fell to the floor with a terrible thump.

Briefly she saw herself battered and still,
And felt herself floating like gossamer till
A shout brought her back to the hospital bed,
Where Amy had briefly been certified dead.
So shocked was the girl by her soul's brief release,
She swore there and then that all jumping would cease.

Now Amy's content with economy flight,
And since her adventure has been more contrite.
She's given up trying to soar like a bird,
A notion that Amy now finds quite absurd.
For unaided flight people simply can't do,
Newtonian laws she had proved to be true.

BASIL BENNETT

"Once upon a time," began Basil's mother,
"A beautiful princess had tried to discover
The thing that was stopping her falling asleep.
She bought a new duvet and tried counting sheep.
Then lifting her mattress the princess could see
That there underneath it was hidden a pea!"

Basil assumed that this story was true,
But just to make sure he resolved what to do.
He looked in the freezer and took out a packet
Of small petit pois which he hid in his jacket.
Then into his parents' dark bedroom he crept
To try out his theory at night as they slept.

But Basil's assessment did not go to plan,
The peas were squashed flat by his parents' divan.
Their terrible sleep wasn't down to the lumps
But unpleasant dampness that gave them goosebumps.
They told their son stories were just an invention.
To prove they were true was too silly to mention!

Hansel and Gretel they read to him next,
But Basil had ended up very perplexed.
He tried eating bits of his house just to see
If windows were sugar and door knobs toffee.
The trips to the dentist to fix his chipped tooth
Cost more than the damage he'd done to the roof.

With Jack and the Beanstalk his parents had found
Their prizewinning runners all chopped to the ground.
"But Daddy I've saved us!" young Basil had said,
"A giant might come while we're lying in bed!"
His father told Basil that giants weren't real,
Nor eggs made of gold for young children to steal.

Despite his keen mind he still couldn't discern
Which stories were real, would the boy never learn?
He checked under bridges for trolls just in case,
And challenged all gingerbread men to a race.
His parents tried hard, but they couldn't convince
Their son that a frog wasn't really a prince.

The boy wasn't dense, all his teachers confirmed,
His grades were first class, they were quite unconcerned.
He'd learned to use logic to seek out the truth,
And tested his theories to lead to a proof.
But strangely the gulf between science and fiction
Eluded the boy, such a tragic affliction!

At last the decision was finally made
To ban fairy stories, and although dismayed,
They read to their boy educational tomes;
Factual books without pixies or gnomes.
And then for a treat that was long overdue,
They went for an outing to visit the zoo.

Alas, the idea though terribly thoughtful,
Created a scene that was gruesome and awful.
On reaching the cage with some huge grizzly bears,
The lad climbed the fence and was caught unawares.
He thought he'd find porridge and three types of bed,
But sadly was eaten and ended up dead.

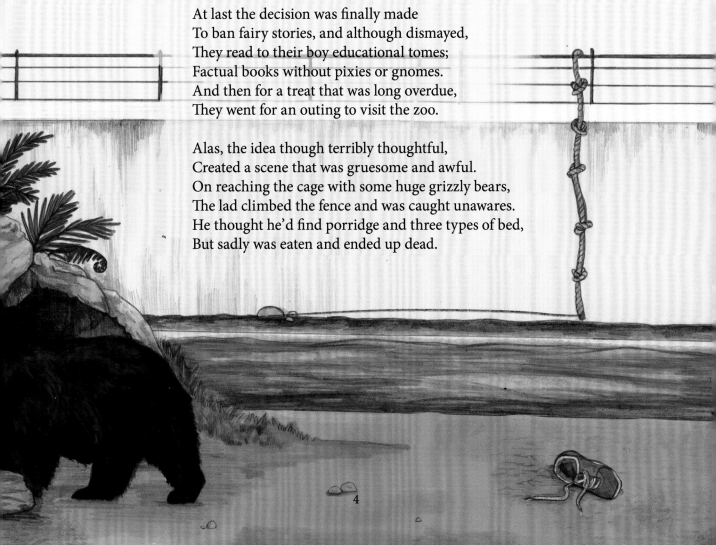

CLARA POPPLETON-BROWN

Clara was always extremely susceptible
To every bizarre and unusual comestible,
Like emu egg omelette and confit of leek,
Or truffle lasagne with roast chicken beak.
She only ate food if it sounded refined,
While pizza or chips she politely declined.

Her notable uncle, a famous food critic,
Thought Clara's refinement was rather terrific.
New foods that most children would simply not try
Young Clara enjoyed with an audible sigh
Of utter contentment, her taste was sublime!
She even liked mackerel topped off with a lime.

He took her to restaurants and places to schmooze
With Michelin stars and tremendous reviews.
To places renowned for all things gastronomic,
Where prices of starters were quite astronomic.
The pair reserved tables at London's best venues
And sampled the most esoteric of menus.

Soon Clara decided to blog while she ate,
Her mother just sighed as she filled the girl's plate.
She watched with concern what her daughter was eating
And called Clara's uncle to ask for a meeting.
Until she knew more of the risks to digestion
More restaurant visits were out of the question!

The trouble with such epicurean excess,
Were Clara's opinions she'd start to express.
She wrote snide reviews of her mother's home cooking
And mocked every dish for not being good looking.
Unless it was served with a drizzle of jus,
Young Poppleton-Brown said it just wouldn't do.

Her uncle was sorry and promised to help
By singing the praises of spinach and kelp.
He told his young niece that such clean eating trends
Were healthy and wholesome, the means to an end!
In truth uncle Don hoped she'd quickly get bored,
Returning to foods that she'd always adored.

But Clara took note as a true devotee,
She even drank spinach and kelp herbal tea.
But as the weeks passed she grew thinner and thinner,
With nothing but greens for her lunch and her dinner.
Avoiding all sugar and protein and fat,
The poor girl would faint at the drop of a hat.

Her mother implored her to eat something nice,
A stew or ragu with some dumplings or rice?
Her daughter smiled weakly, and grimaced in pain,
For spinach and kelp do odd things to your brain.
She thanked her poor mother and went up to bed,
Where, sorry to say, she was later found dead.

Now eating in restaurants with five-star reviews
Is one of life's pleasures that few would refuse,
But too much fine dining can soon become tedious,
And few can find pleasure in being abstemious.
So eat what you like but embrace moderation,
Without the extremes of excess and privation.

DESMOND SLAPWORTHY

When Desmond was born, the midwife had fumbled,
She said she was sorry, but somehow she stumbled
Exactly as Desmond came slithering out,
He slipped through her hands, she had no time to shout!
He bungee jumped on his umbilical cord,
As chaos ensued on the hospital ward.

This fall was a portent for Desmond's young life,
Until he was three it was nothing but strife.
Baths were disastrous - he practically drowned,
Floundering and kicking and flapping around.
And when he tried crawling, he skidded and slid,
He couldn't stay upright, whatever he did.

Some eminent doctors examined his hearing
And found lots of wax that they thought needed clearing.
Perhaps it affected the lad's inner ear?
They hoped that in time it would just disappear.
But meanwhile young Desmond kept falling from heights,
Giving his mother some terrible frights.

From beds he had tumbled and broken his arm,
Just lying down lengthways could cause the boy harm.
So stairs were all gated in case he should roam,
And furniture edges all covered in foam.
His cot was designed like a small prison cell,
The bars close together in case the lad fell.

Now toddlers are programmed to run and explore,
But Desmond would trip as he walked through the door.
A scooter was sadly quite out of the question,
'Avoid things with wheels' was his teacher's suggestion.
So roller skates, skateboards and bikes were off limits,
He'd crash and fall off in a matter of minutes.

The problem of balance was clearly compounded
By not holding on, a trait that confounded
His parents and teachers and friends and relations:
"Hang on!" and "Be careful!" their loud exhortations.
If only the boy had a prehensile tail
To grip onto every available rail.

The poor lad was clumsy, the facts bore it out,
Whatever the sport he would always wipe out.
Each game that he played was a clear demonstration
That Desmond could only excel at prostration.
The only two pastimes where Desmond could shine
Were football and swimming, where diving was fine.

One year they went skiing to try him on snow.
Strapped flat on a sledge they attempted to tow
Young Desmond up quite a small nursery slope,
But after five minutes they'd given up hope.
Attached to a tether his speed had increased,
Till hitting a mogul he shot off the piste.

As soon as the hospital discharged the lad,
A trip up to Lapland was planned by his dad.
A treat to make up for the skiing disaster,
(Which needless to say he would never have mastered).
So off to the Arctic the two of them flew,
And there Desmond's wish to see Santa came true.

A huge golden sleigh stood with reindeer grazing,
Which Desmond ran up to, this trip was amazing!
But Desmond fell down as he climbed in the sleigh,
Which upset the reindeer who bolted away.
Poor Desmond flew out as they lurched round a bend,
Straight into a pine tree, and that was the end.

ERNEST GURNING

Ernest Gurning was known for his greed,
Gulping and chomping with terrible speed.
He chewed only once before trying to swallow,
And with every mouthful another would follow.
Those watching him eat were disgusted to note
The volume of food he could stuff down his throat.

When Ernest sat down at the table to eat,
The first thing to go were the pieces of meat.
Drumsticks and wings were consumed in one bite,
With bones and the skin (which was hardly polite).
While burgers and steaks were devoured at a rate
So fast that he sometimes bit into the plate!

Then after his meat he would start on the vegetables,
Gorging his way through a range of comestibles,
Shovelled at speed into Ernest's great maw
(Along with the bits that he'd dropped on the floor).
His greasy long fingers helped food on its way,
For cutlery simply caused Ernest delay.

Family mealtimes were pointless affairs,
For as they sat down with much scraping of chairs,
Young Gurning would finish before they could start,
And burp very loudly or end with a fart.
His face smeared with food and his clothes stained with sauces,
The boy would protest when he ran out of courses.

Of course this would normally make you quite fat,
But not for young Gurning, whose stomach was flat.
Whatever he did, his weight wouldn't increase,
He didn't appear in the least bit obese!
Nor had he been sick (quite a common assumption)
When people are thin after massive consumption.

The doctors ran tests to determine the cause,
It just wasn't normal to eat without pause.
But having examined young Ernest's digestion,
A surgical route was their only suggestion.
His thyroid was something they'd like to reduce,
But Ernest refused, this was surely abuse!

No closer to curing the cause of his maladies,
They couldn't reduce Ernest's intake of calories.
His parents hid biscuits and locked the fridge door,
But Ernest broke in with a circular saw.
Until the day came he would seal his own fate,
A tragic result of the way that he ate.

Now Ernest loved gardening, a noble pursuit,
And skilled was the boy in the growing of fruit.
Till one day he swallowed a peach, stone and all,
A gluttonous act that would be his downfall.
For Ernest's oesophagus though freakishly wide,
Was finally blocked and the boy promptly died.

FANNY LAVENDER-LOVELACE

Some teenagers don't follow modern convention,
They don't dream of fame or seek endless attention.
They meet friends in person and read real books,
And care about kindness not how someone looks.
They steer their own course and don't need validation
From comments or likes to confirm admiration.

Fanny was one such unorthodox teen.
From waking to bedtime she'd often be seen
High up in a tree or else splashing in streams,
Exploring the world and pursuing her dreams.
Her parents adored their rebellious child,
Who grew up untethered and wonderfully wild.

At home she camped out on a bed of dry leaves
Stuffed into a sack which she kept in the eaves.
Her pillow was moss that was mixed up with heather,
(It did get quite damp in extremely wet weather).
But Fanny slept well in the nest she had made;
Lulled by the wind and an owl's serenade.

At dawn she'd wake up and ablute in the pond,
A ritual of which she'd become rather fond.
Untangling hair with a brush made of thistles,
Or combs that were fashioned from old hedgehog bristles.
And then it was time to attend to her teeth,
With toothpaste she made from a peppermint leaf.

For breakfast she sat down to nuts, seeds and berries,
A glass of fresh milk and a bowlful of cherries.
No sugary hoops or some toast spread with chocolate,
These things were expensive and horribly profligate!
In short, she lived simply, avoiding those foods
That caused diabetes and sugar rush moods.

School was a problem for Fanny of course,
Her dad dropped her off on the back of a horse!
And uniform sadly was not as prescribed,
She wouldn't wear socks which her classmates decried.
She didn't like ties and her shirt was constricting,
Her views and the teachers' were always conflicting.

Some children made fun of her, called her a sprite,
But Fanny just laughed and would not pick a fight.
She pitied their lives ruled by iPads and phones,
And make-up to mimic celebrity clones.
They couldn't climb trees or distinguish a bird,
She thought that their interests were rather absurd.

Then one day young Fanny became quite unwell,
A bite from a spider had started to swell.
Her temperature soared and her palms were too hot,
She didn't want medicine, she thought it was rot.
She made a herb poultice with bark from a beech,
And tried to get well with the help of a leech.

Her parents objected, but to no avail,
And Fanny collapsed having gone very pale.
The leech was so hungry, it quickly consumed
Two pints of her blood which it fed to its brood.
Poor Fanny thus emptied of cells red and white,
Died peacefully late on a dark autumn night.

Living a life that was simple and clean
Has many advantages, as you have seen,
But medical treatment is much more effective
Than leeches, whose uses are often selective.
If only the girl had a tetanus injection,
She wouldn't have died from a simple infection.

GEORGE GOULDEN-GLOOM

When George had gone missing he'd soon be discovered
Inside a large trunk or curled up in a cupboard.
Not to leap out so his mother would jump,
Or as a response to a juvenile grump,
He simply enjoyed being out of the light;
Like bats, owls and hamsters he woke up at night.

His fondness for darkness became problematic.
He carried umbrellas and slept in the attic
With blinds on the windows to block out the glare,
And sunglasses worn when he went anywhere.
His parents' concerns grew increasingly vocal;
Was George a recluse or just plain antisocial?

When asked, George would shrug and would say very little,
He said that his dad shouldn't worry and whittle.
It wasn't a subject he tried to evade,
He wasn't dissembling, he needed the shade!
His dad sent his case to an medical journal
To understand more about being nocturnal.

Poor George always tried to avoid being missed,
But finding dark places he couldn't resist!
He'd open a drawer which was full of old clothes,
And tuck up beneath them to have a quick doze.
Or under the bed he would crawl with delight,
To lie very still with his eyes screwed up tight.

Then one summer solstice he took it too far,
By locking himself in the boot of the car.
He hadn't considered his own suffocation;
The inky black confines were such a temptation!
Despite this near miss the boy wouldn't desist,
So child psychiatrists came to assist.

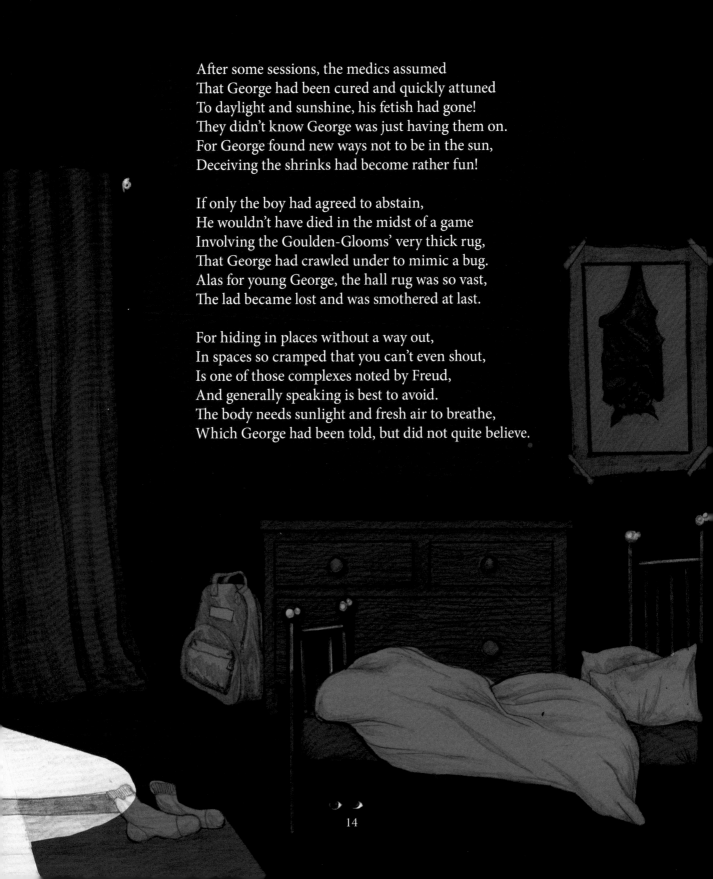

After some sessions, the medics assumed
That George had been cured and quickly attuned
To daylight and sunshine, his fetish had gone!
They didn't know George was just having them on.
For George found new ways not to be in the sun,
Deceiving the shrinks had become rather fun!

If only the boy had agreed to abstain,
He wouldn't have died in the midst of a game
Involving the Goulden-Glooms' very thick rug,
That George had crawled under to mimic a bug.
Alas for young George, the hall rug was so vast,
The lad became lost and was smothered at last.

For hiding in places without a way out,
In spaces so cramped that you can't even shout,
Is one of those complexes noted by Freud,
And generally speaking is best to avoid.
The body needs sunlight and fresh air to breathe,
Which George had been told, but did not quite believe.

14

HECTOR HORATIO-HOTLY

Horatio-Hotly had very strong views
On people and places and things in the news.
He hated all game shows and sport he despised;
Political leaders were often chastised.
No one escaped young Horatio's rants,
Not grown-ups or children or teen miscreants.

One morning at breakfast, by way of example,
His mother had asked him to try a small sample
Of blueberry jam that she'd lovingly made.
He gave her a broadside, a full on tirade:
"This fruit is from Spain!" barked the boy with a squint,
"Do you know what this means for our carbon footprint?"

He never held back from his blunt observations,
His life was afflicted by endless frustrations!
Gum-chewers, litterers, bad punctuation,
Fat people, thin people, noisy gustation.
He sighed and he tutted while shaking his head,
Just being in public would make him see red.

Hector was tactless and very loquacious,
He went on and on, oh that boy was audacious!
He angered those listening with every address,
But Hector Horatio couldn't care less.
His values were firm and his oratory loud,
The boy was obnoxious and horribly proud.

"Your views are ridiculous!" Hector would sneer
At radio talk shows (though no one could hear),
Shouting at callers whose views he deplored,
And facile DJs whose style he abhorred.
There wasn't a subject he wouldn't debate,
But Hector's belligerence started to grate.

On Facebook he'd lost nearly all of his friends,
Through comments so rude they were bound to offend.
When Twitter had banned him he started a blog:
"The Righteous Tirade of a Young Demagogue."
But most of his time was spent dealing with trolls,
And Hector lost sight of more worthy life goals.

Ranting online meant that Hector missed out,
With no time for playing or messing about.
His homework was late and his teacher complained
That lessons with Hector had got rather strained.
He argued all day as a matter of principle,
Thinking himself to be nigh on invincible.

Then one day he picked on the wrong sort of chap,
A hulk with tattoos and a black baseball cap.
Now Hector despised those who liked to be inked,
And said so quite loudly before he could think.
The man turned around with a furious shout
And landed a punch that would knock Hector out.

Battered and bruised, Hector sagely reflected,
That people's appearance was better respected.
He'd stand up for causes he knew to be right,
And only pick battles he needed to fight.
Some choices and views might not be to his taste,
But life was too short for young Hector to waste.

IDA IMOGEN-IMP

Wast Water's known to be cold, dark and deep,
Surrounded by screes both unstable and steep.
Located up north in the west of the Lakes,
It's quiet because of the time that it takes
To travel on roads that are narrow and slow,
And often get blocked in the winter by snow.

Young Ida was lucky to live in the valley,
And walking back home she would frequently tarry
To climb up a rock face or perilous edge,
Or stand on a summit and perch on a ledge.
She'd bagged all the Wainwrights and Nuttals and Birketts,
Completing the longest, most arduous circuits.

Although only twelve, she'd become well-respected
For races she'd won and the cups she'd collected.
Her athletic skill was quite plain to observe,
But one thing she lacked was a sense of reserve.
She laughed at those entrants who'd fallen or tripped,
And openly mocked those who went ill-equipped.

Worse still was her boasting each time that she won,
Competing with Ida was never much fun.
Then one day a girl who came second requested
They try a triathlon, she even suggested
That Ida might lose? To which Ida replied,
She'd win with her eyes shut (for such was her pride).

In early December a poster went up,
Announcing the Wast Water Challenger Cup.
Now swimming was not one of Ida's great strengths,
She swam very fast but she couldn't do lengths.
The thought of a dip in an unheated lake
Made Ida go pale and her knees start to shake.

Yet having been challenged she craved more success,
And duly signed up, hoping soon to impress
The rows of spectators who'd shout, yell and cheer.
The thought of her winning dispelled any fear.
She banished all thought of the race from her mind,
Until the day dawned and she pulled up her blind.

The weather was shocking, a squall had set in,
The worst kind of weather to go for a swim!
She went to the start looking down at the lake,
And realised she'd made a tremendous mistake.
The flag was held up and a whistle was blown,
The others dived in and left Ida alone.

Emitting a cry, Ida jumped off the pier,
And everyone watched the young girl disappear.
Shocked by the cold, Ida's heart had stopped dead,
And down she had sunk like an ingot of lead.
Her body was later retrieved by a diver
Who didn't succeed when he tried to revive her.

Games, sports and pastimes are not life or death,
It's OK to lose or to be out of breath.
What matters is that you compete with good grace,
Have fun and enjoy it wherever your place.
And if you have genuine sporting ability,
Remember to win with a touch of humility.

JAMES AMERSHAM-PHIPPS

James started school with a passion for science.
Boycotting art, he once said in defiance:
"Painting is fine for those sorts who can draw,
But most of the artists I know are a bore!
Better to prove something, try a new theory,
Than sketch some old fruit, which is awfully dreary."

James lived at home with a distant relation,
As both of his parents worked on the space station.
The boy watched it fly through the heavens at night,
Passing above him in orbital flight.
He waved at the dot as it sped on its way,
And vowed that he'd fly in a rocket one day.

So James spent his days learning complex mathematics,
Picking up physics and tricky quadratics.
He pored over textbooks and complex equations,
Ignoring his teachers oft-said lamentations
That pupils should aim to be much more well-rounded,
A view that James questioned and said was ill-founded.

In truth he found chemistry more to his liking,
A subject for which his adeptness was striking.
He quickly absorbed books on atoms and elements,
And made noxious compounds while doing experiments
With metals that burned when exposed to the air.
The house smelt for days when young James singed his hair!

In August, his parents returned from a mission
To learn that their son had been working on fission.
He'd wanted to find a new means of propulsion,
A quest that had led to young James' expulsion
For blowing a hole in the wall of his school,
While making his own TNT molecule.

He also confessed to a minor infraction
Involving a dubious online transaction,
Where James had obtained a few grams of plutonium,
Some lye and a kilo of unrefined sodium.
The MI5 agents were not very pleased,
They raided his house and his stockpile was seized.

His parents however did not seem to mind,
For James said the chemicals he had combined
Would make a miraculous new type of fuel,
That changed the agenda and broke every rule.
If James's invention succeeded in trials,
Then mankind could travel for millions of miles!

To mark his discovery, they took from the shelf
A bottle of vodka to toast his good health.
They let their son James take a moderate sip,
And watched with alarm as it fizzed on his lip.
He clutched at his throat and soon started to shake,
They didn't know James had drunk lye by mistake!

He'd poured out the booze while concocting his fuel
And hadn't re-labelled the bottle, the fool!
If only he'd marked it and locked it away,
Perhaps he'd have gone into orbit one day.
Instead the boy died from his deadly libation
Because of a terrible miscalculation.

KATE WENDLEBURY-WHIM*

*Metre change!

Roberto the Magnificent picked up his only daughter,
And threw her from the platform edge into a pool of water.
The water she was aiming for was only inches deep,
But down she dived, her arms outstretched in one enormous leap.
The crowd screamed out and shut their eyes with sharp intakes of breath,
But Kate had landed gracefully, she'd cheated certain death!

Roberto's Circus was their home, a place of entertainments,
With jugglers, clowns and acrobats all wearing golden raiments.
They toured the world to rave reviews enjoying wealth and fame,
Their show got better every year, it never was the same:
A strongman with a chest of iron, a girl who climbed one-handed,
A monkey speaking Mandarin, their repertoire expanded.

Kate was happy flying high in airborne feats of daring,
Her father coached her night and day, it was the perfect pairing.
She swung from ropes and climbed up ladders forty-metres high,
And launched herself into the air, it seemed that she could fly!
"So graceful," said those looking up who watched her swing and swoop,
"I've never seen such bravery, she did a loop-the-loop!"

Then on one of her practice runs, she lost her concentration,
Her fingers missed the catcher's hand, a one-off aberration!
She landed on the floor below and broke her hip and spine,
Then shouted: "I can touch my nose, I'm sure that I'll be fine!"
The medics who attended didn't take her at her word,
They put her on a stretcher as they worriedly conferred.

The hospital ran lots of tests to ascertain the damage,
With X-rays, CTs, MRIs, as much as they could manage.
Poor Kate was put in traction while cocooned in lots of plaster,
She knew that for an acrobat this could be a disaster.
Eventually the tests came back with full and frank analysis,
Her spinal cord had been compressed, and caused long-term paralysis.

Then after months of failed attempts at rehabilitation,
She called a halt and made her peace with Anger and Frustration.
Instead she looked at other ways to practise and perform,
Determined that she'd soon be back to take the world by storm.
Her sense of timing made her think that juggling could be good,
So every day she practised with some clubs made out of wood.

Before too long the girl had mastered balls and clubs and rings,
Not three or four but five and six, they flew as if on strings!
And though she couldn't move about the stage to make a catch,
Her throws were true and so precise she never had to snatch.
One year went by and back she went to join Roberto's troop,
Her wheelchair came in down a ramp and through a flaming hoop.

The people stood and clapped and cheered and Kate looked quite relaxed,
As up she threw into the air a hammer, saw and axe.
Those deadly items spun and sliced their way into the sky,
Before the axe came down too fast and struck her in the eye.
She died at once, I'm sad to say, right there upon the stage.
A tragic end for one so skilled at such a tender age.

LEO PRICKLETON-PATCH

Leo always played the fool, a truly naughty boy,
Whose antics in the playground would invariably annoy
The staff who had to deal with his behaviour every day,
It wasn't always what he did, but rather what he'd say.
He'd goad his fellow pupils and incite them to do wrong,
Or swear and tell rude jokes or mock his teachers in a song.

In history he didn't see the value of the past,
His ignorance of times gone by left everyone aghast.
"What's the point of learning about people who are dead?
I'd rather read a magazine or play a game instead!"
In science Leo cut up frogs and threw them at his friends,
And made a range of peashooters by using ballpoint pens.

In English lessons Leo tore out pages from his books,
Making paper aeroplanes and getting filthy looks
From pupils trying hard to master Chaucer, Keats and Joyce,
While Leo only learned to read because he had no choice.
His teachers reprimanded him and stood him on a stool;
The stupid boy thought ignorance had made him rather cool.

Leo's parents spoke to him, explained the implications
Of endless pranks and failed exams, a woeful situation!
They thought he'd always wanted to become an astronaut?
But Leo didn't listen and their lecture came to naught.
He crossed his arms and said that school was such a waste of time,
He'd get a proper job one day, and said that he'd be fine.

Meanwhile his headteacher tried her best to find a way
To keep him on the straight and narrow, even for a day.
Perhaps he'd flourish if they gave the boy a job to do?
Being made a house captain could lead to a breakthrough.
Her staff refused to ratify these plans for his promotion,
He'd be a despot, rule by fear, just think of the commotion!

So Leo went from bad to worse, and oh the tricks he played!
Like butter on the door handles, a flour-filled grenade.
He threw it in the staff room as the teachers had their break,
The noise of it was deafening, it made the windows shake!
And then there was the incident involving Leo's pet,
A snake that ate his teacher's keys, they had to call the vet!

His final misdemeanour was a stunt so asinine,
He asked his friend to film it and then post the clip online.
He'd seen a young magician by the name of Thomas Lax
Consume a bag of broken glass and swallow fifty tacks.
So Leo bought some drawing pins, which sadly weren't a prop,
Made out of brass, he bought them from a local paper shop.

Suffice to say the trick went wrong as Leo choked them down,
They punctured his oesophagus and shut his liver down.
His friend who filmed the escapade assumed it was an act,
As blood (or ketchup) seemed to ooze from his digestive tract.
But Leo's screams were genuine as was his expiration,
All caught on film which soon became an internet sensation.

MAUD OSTLETHWAITE-PLUM

Maud lived in Sydney along with her mother,
Two cats and a dog and her good-looking brother,
Who spent his days sailing or cleaning his boat,
He liked nothing more than just being afloat.
But Maud disliked water, though raised on the coast,
A fact she denied, for young Maud liked to boast.

Maud was the last in a long line of sailors,
Who went to Australia working as whalers.
Within a few months they had all settled down,
And quickly established a sizeable town
That thrived on the business of fishing and whaling,
(Which back in the day wasn't seen as a failing).

The first of the Plums was exalted by all,
A bearded Goliath some seven-feet tall.
Old Malen would stand at the wheel like a rock
Through towering seas as he sailed to the dock.
His home was the ocean, it ran in his bones,
They said of old Malen he knew Davy Jones!

A hundred years later young Maud had been born
As dawn was just breaking one dark winter's morn.
A storm shook the cottage and waves lashed the shore,
While old Malen's ghost kept a watch at the door.
He looked at the baby curled up on its mother,
A seafarer surely, just like her big brother.

But as you have heard, though she lived by the sea,
Sailing was not really Maud's cup of tea.
She always felt seasick and frankly got bored,
While surfing was something she simply abhorred.
Paddling and floating around for a swell,
Had always made Maud feel extremely unwell.

Needless to say that her friends didn't know
That all of her bragging was just done for show.
She said she went surfing some five days a week,
And lied when she spoke of her carving technique.
Then late in September her bluff would be called
By Ivy, a girl who had listened enthralled.

As Maud sat cross-legged, recounting more lies,
Young Ivy sat breathless and gazed in her eyes.
She asked Maud to teach her, to act as her guide,
And Maud said she would, as she swelled up with pride.
So later that week they met up on the beach,
Where Maud, now reluctantly, started to teach.

She paddled to sea with her student in tow,
Not feeling the riptide that raced past below.
She tried to stand up but fell off and was swept
Away from her board, oh that girl was inept!
She screamed out in fear and it seemed she was lost,
Her lying had come at a terrible cost.

Ivy thought quickly and phoned the coastguard,
Paddling back had been desperately hard.
Then Maud heard a shout from the beach, could it be?
Her brother was coming, that much she could see.
He battled the riptide with each mighty stroke,
But Maud was too far and he hadn't a hope.

Ivy and Maud were picked up safe and sound;
Her brother, I'm sorry to say, had been drowned.
Soon after this Maud moved away from the coast,
But found she was followed by old Malen's ghost,
Who stood by her bed every night of the week,
To wake the girl up with a blood-curdling shriek.

NEVILLE DEVEREAUX-CRIPPS

Neville D-C was a fortunate boy,
Whose bedroom contained every possible toy:
A tractor, a trailer, a working space rocket,
A voice-controlled plane you could fit in your pocket.
Toys that his parents could barely afford,
Yet Devereaux-Cripps still complained he was bored.

His mother was baffled, it didn't make sense,
Had presents they'd given caused Neville offence?
They hoped that his mood was no more than a phase,
But Neville remained in the depths of malaise.
Games, toys and gadgets of every sort
Were held in contempt, or dismissed with a snort.

Perhaps it was better to get the boy reading,
So with the best novels his parents tried feeding
Young Neville's grey matter with stories enlightening,
Adventures and classics and books that were frightening.
But Neville appeared to be quite uninspired,
He yawned and he sighed and he said he was tired.

If books didn't do it, perhaps nature would?
Experts professed that fresh air did you good.
"It's cold and it's wet!" moaned their obstinate child,
(Although it was summer and balmy and mild).
He told them he'd rather be up in his room
To stare at the ceiling till mid-afternoon.

For Neville delighted in being inactive,
Long bouts of inertia he found most attractive.
He didn't like walking or going too far,
A trip round the corner required a car.
His sister predicted that ongoing apathy
Could cause irreversible muscular atrophy!

His parents agreed and became more tenacious,
They wouldn't give up though they found it vexatious.
So taking the plunge they enrolled him on courses:
Karate and tennis and riding on horses.
They filled every minute he spent out of school
With football or rugby or hours of boules.

Neville was shocked and refused to attend,
He feigned he was ill and once tried to pretend
He'd been agoraphobic, a nasty affliction,
With multiple symptoms of every description.
His parents ignored him and took him regardless,
Which Neville protested was utterly heartless.

They tried him with every improving pursuit,
But weeks of this regimen didn't bear fruit.
The boy had rebelled and he wouldn't take part,
They couldn't just force him, they hadn't the heart!
So Neville was left there to maunder and mope,
They'd reached a dead end and had given up hope.

Neville epitomised wasted potential,
A life that would prove to be inconsequential.
He squandered good fortune that life had provided;
Ambition was something he mocked and derided.
He wouldn't take part in the great human race,
And finally left it with hardly a trace.

OLIVE TIPPLESWITCH*

*Metre change!

Olive was obsessed with JK Rowling's Harry Potter,
Hermione was her nom de plume, she wrote it on her jotter.
She wore a cloak each day to school and made up lots of spells,
Mixing potions, drawing runes and causing noxious smells.
Her teachers wished she'd spend her time on more established lessons,
Instead she practised alchemy and incantation sessions.

Her classmates found her rather weird and left her well alone,
She wrote her essays with a quill and didn't have a phone!
Olive claimed telepathy was cheaper and far better,
But failing that she'd use an owl to send her friends a letter.
The fact she never mastered even one successful spell,
Didn't worry Olive, who was sure she would excel.

She persevered day and night to learn about Dark Arts,
Her pin-up was Professor Snape, she'd memorised the parts
In all the books that dealt with curses dangerous and grim,
Or scenes where Harry used his wand (she had a crush on him)!
'Expelliamus' shouted Olive, using wands she'd made
From chopsticks, dowels and twigs she'd whittled with a razor blade.

Olive's fascination with such supernatural things
As dragons, trolls and magic charms or mushroom fairy rings,
Turned her bedroom into a repository for clutter,
But would she clear it up? Not she! It made her parents mutter,
That Hogwarts pupils wouldn't live in such an awful mess,
So Olive said she'd tidy up (though under some duress).

In truth the girl was lazy when it came to doing chores.
She never washed up, folded socks or vacuumed any floors.
Not only that, but like so many children of her age,
She didn't ask to borrow things, which caused parental rage.
And if that wasn't bad enough, when items were returned,
Quite often they were broken, bent or sometimes even burned!

Olive had been banned from taking things without permission,
She moaned and sulked and railed against this unfair imposition.
But one day when alone she snapped her most beloved wand,
A piece of bamboo cane of which the girl was very fond.
So with her father's bunch of keys, she went into his shed,
And standing on a box of tiles, she reached above her head.

There hanging on the wall was every sort of useful tool,
A hammer, saw and screwdriver, a four-foot metal rule.
Then dangling by a tenon saw she found the perfect thing,
A pointy piece of metal with a handle wrapped in string.
Unbeknownst to Olive, what she'd taken was an awl,
A tool for punching leather that would soon be her downfall.

Brandishing her wand aloft she shouted 'Voldemort!'
"I've come to stop your fiendish plans, which I alone can thwart!"
She dodged and parried with the awl while straddling a broom,
Pretending she was flying as she ran into her room.
But as she burst in through the door she tripped upon a shoe,
And fell headlong onto her awl, which ran the girl right through.

Death by misadventure was the coroner's report,
Brought about by loss of blood that cut her young life short.
No magic spells or mandrake roots could bring the poor girl back,
Not Dumbledore, McGonegall or even Sirius Black.
If only Olive Tippleswitch had tidied up her room,
She'd be alive pretending to play Quidditch on a broom.

PRUE FOOTLEBURY-JONES

Prue had grown haughty and terribly vain,
She looked down on people with snobbish disdain.
A trait she had learned from a pompous relation
(Who back in the day had been quite a sensation).
Aunt Scarlett bought Prue such extravagant things,
Like clothes from Armani and Tiffany rings.

"No outfits from Tesco or second-hand toys,
For flaunting your labels is one of life's joys."
Her aunt reassured her, "It's sort of a sport."
(Another 'life lesson' Aunt Scarlett had taught)!
"It shows you have breeding, a sign of your status.
Those poor common people, no wonder they hate us!"

Her mother and father sat down with their daughter
To try and undo what Aunt Scarlett had taught her.
They showed her that labels were largely a sham,
A way to hike prices, a marketing scam!
While some brands were worth it and certainly finer,
The bulk were all made in the same part of China.

Her parents' good sense led to tantrums and tears,
The girl was determined to outdo her peers.
Her aunt's inculcation had been unremitting,
And Prue had accepted, completely unwitting,
Aunt Scarlett's long list of the things she would need.
She soon had the same predilection for greed.

Each Christmas and birthday became an ordeal
For both of Prue's parents, who started to feel
That nothing they bought for their daughter would do,
She'd be disappointed, a fact that they knew
Was caused by Aunt Scarlett's immoderate spending.
They told her to stop, but it seemed never-ending!

Then one day Aunt Scarlett's largesse caused a scene
Involving young Prue, who had just turned sixteen.
They went off at dawn to browse Selfridges' sale,
And queued up for hours in the midst of a gale.
And what, you may ask, were they hoping to snag?
Some shoes by Manolo with matching handbag.

But when the doors opened, a stampede ensued.
"But we were here first, oh how horribly rude!"
Complained Prue quite loudly as people pushed past.
"We stood there for ages and now we're in last!"
Aunt Scarlett was punched as she fought for a skirt,
While Prue was knocked over and seriously hurt.

As Prue lay in hospital badly concussed,
The thought of the brawl filled the girl with disgust.
She'd no longer care if her aunt was impressed
By how much things cost or the way that she dressed.
What mattered were memories, made with her friends,
Not brand names or labels or transitory trends.

QUENTIN CUMBERPATCH

Quentin was born on a farm outside Leeds,
A smallholding famous for rare cattle breeds.
Vaynols and Chillinghams bred to compete,
And Aberdeen-Anguses sold for their meat.
The farm quickly grew and the herd was expanded,
But such rapid growth left his father short-handed.

Then one day at breakfast, young Quentin suggested
He'd take on the jobs that his father detested.
He didn't mind muck and was good with a broom,
He'd clean up the yard, even tidy his room.
So keen was the lad that his father agreed,
And Quentin was put to work measuring feed.

Quentin worked hard at the tasks he was set,
And even tried calving to help out the vet.
They worked in the cowshed late into the night
With Quentin attentively shining a light,
And helping to clean a new calf with some straw,
That came out all slimy and covered with gore.

"You must be so proud," said the vet to his dad.
"I am," he replied, "though I sometimes feel bad
For taking advantage of such dedication,
It's not really helping his school education.
His reading is poor and his writing appalling,
The thing he excels at is hedging and walling!

But Quentin did not have much time for his schooling,
For work on the farm was incredibly gruelling.
His teachers said farming though noble and good,
Was not the best path in his early childhood.
Reading and writing were skills that he needed.
Without them, his progress would soon be impeded!

His father agreed but the farm was so manic,
That working alone made old Cumberpatch panic.
He'd grown to rely on his hard-working son.
The farm was successful, efficiently run.
So Quentin was given more onerous chores,
Beyond mucking-out and the sweeping of floors.

One day as he entered a door in the yard,
The boy saw a sign, but the words were too hard.
The writing was clear but he struggled to read,
It listed equipment for breathing he'd need,
Plus rescue procedures and hazard prevention,
And chemical symbols too complex to mention.

As Quentin pumped out a huge tank full of slurry,
The lad felt unwell, so he started to hurry.
He didn't know cow pats on such a large scale,
Cause gases to form in a deadly cocktail.
Poor Quentin grew dizzy, began to perspire,
Then fainted and fell, sinking down in the mire.

The farmer was fined and his business shut down
By safety inspectors, who said with a frown
That children should not be employed on a farm,
Too great are the risks and potential for harm.
Learning to read was a vital foundation
That may have prevented the boy's suffocation.

RHODA HENTWISTLE

Rhoda sat still as she gazed at her screen,
Amazed and astonished by what she had seen.
Apparently, under the earth's rocky crust,
Were rivers of lava, the girl was nonplussed!
The world was a jigsaw of big floating plates,
All shifting and moving at very slow rates.

The more that she studied the laws of tectonics,
The more she was prone to severe histrionics.
This led to her contacting six volcanologists,
Along with professors and famous geologists,
Who said with conviction (and some sensitivity)
That death was not likely from seismic activity.

But Rhoda looked out of her window with fear,
Her view of the Cairngorms was awfully clear.
How did they know that these towering mountains
Would not spew out lava in fiery fountains
Of ash, molten magma and sulphurous gas?
She trembled and fretted, the poor little lass.

Young Rhoda's affliction became so extreme,
She dreamt of volcanoes, and started to scream
If planes flew nearby or a truck rumbled past,
Convinced that her home would be hit by a blast
Of burning hot rocks raining down on the roof.
She'd read it online so she didn't need proof!

To conquer her fears, Rhoda's parents decided
They'd climb a volcano (however misguided).
"We're told," they assured her, "that though it feels drastic,
This therapy works for all things pyroclastic.
We'll start with some films to build up your exposure,
Just trust us, you'll quickly regain your composure."

Eventually off to Mount Etna they went,
Despite Rhoda's pleading, they wouldn't relent.
They boarded a bus up the volcano's flanks,
Past hillsides of lava and steep wooded banks,
Until the bus stopped and the group disembarked
On ground that was steaming and deeply pockmarked.

Rhoda looked up at her parents and cried,
"You said I'd feel better, you tricked me, you lied!"
"Come on," they implored her, "let's go to the top,
This fear of volcanoes must come to a stop!"
So onward they climbed as the smoke trickled out,
But Rhoda ran off with a terrified shout.

"Don't move!" yelled their guide, "you're approaching a vent!"
But Rhoda continued her reckless descent.
Then hydrogen sulphide got into her nose,
As Rhoda stood next to some deep magma flows.
She fainted and fell and was quickly cremated,
And so, for poor Rhoda, her life was truncated.

In truth Rhoda needn't have died in this way,
But science and research could never allay
A phobia based on the nonsense she'd read,
On websites that fuelled her irrational dread.
A trip to Mount Etna would not have been needed,
If expert advice had been properly heeded.

SUSAN SHUTTERBUCK

A hideous scream could be heard through the house,
The sort often caused by a spider or mouse.
But this one was coming from Susan, whose shriek
Was born not of fear, but a bad fit of pique.
She'd asked for a sweet and her parents refused.
You'd think from the noise that the girl was abused!

For Susan would yell at the drop of a hat,
There's no use denying, the girl was a brat!
If told to sit still at the table to eat,
She'd kick off at once and lash out with her feet.
While gentle requests to put on her pyjamas,
Would usually lead to some harrowing dramas.

Yes, life with the girl was a battle of wills.
The doctor prescribed both her parents some pills.
To offset the trauma of life with their daughter,
They bribed her with toys, but the things that they bought her
Were 'stupid' or 'boring', which led to more tears.
Oh what could be done, it had gone on for years!

Each day Susan practised new ways to transgress,
Deliberately causing her parents distress.
Things that they asked her were always unfair,
She'd stick out her tongue or she'd growl like a bear.
Attempts to use reasoning, tact and persuasion,
Were met with defiance on every occasion.

Her father tried hard to be patient and kind,
And read up on ailments affecting the mind.
Perhaps there was something amiss with her brain,
Or were all these tantrums a symptom of pain?
The doctors confessed that they hadn't a clue,
Then therapists tried before giving up too.

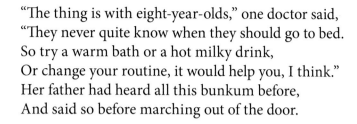

"The thing is with eight-year-olds," one doctor said,
"They never quite know when they should go to bed.
So try a warm bath or a hot milky drink,
Or change your routine, it would help you, I think."
Her father had heard all this bunkum before,
And said so before marching out of the door.

Then things took a turn for the worse late in June,
When Susan was ordered to go to her room
For kicking the cat, when it got in her way.
"How cruel and unkind Susan, what do you say?"
She didn't say much, blowing raspberries instead,
Refusing steadfastly to go up to bed.

So Susan was picked up and carried upstairs,
Bawling and screaming and knocking down chairs.
They left the girl wailing alone in her room;
Her parents' grey faces a picture of gloom.
They sat in the living room listening until
The howling subsided, and things became still.

They couldn't have known that her terrible rage
Had brought on a seizure, despite her young age.
For anger has side-effects, that much is clear,
High blood pressure being the first to appear.
Bad temper unchecked can be deadly unless,
You learn to relax and eliminate stress.

TITUS MONTGOMERY-BANG

Titus Montgomery was one of those boys,
Who loved to repurpose all manner of toys,
To build things the maker had never intended,
Like crayons and felt tips that ended up blended,
Or cars he attempted to melt in the fire,
To turn into ingots and stretch into wire.

The boy never thought of the trouble he'd cause
By unscrewing handles from all of the doors,
Or using his school shoes as beds for his pets,
Or turning some tights into long fishing nets.
"Boys will be boys", his great-grandmother said,
Till Titus unwittingly burned down her shed.

His brother Andronicus followed his lead,
Persuaded to emulate every misdeed.
But Titus was eldest, and should have known better,
Or so said his mother when Titus upset her.
At school his headteacher considered suspension
When Titus unveiled his latest invention.

"Today, during history, Titus decided
That Tudors were boring, he even confided
He favoured the Romans and brave gladiators,
Who wrestled with lions and live alligators.
He spent the whole lesson pretending to fight,
With swords that he made from a fluorescent light!

We value his knowledge and technical skills,
His sense of adventure (which frequently thrills),
But such an obsession for re-engineering
Will lead to an accident, that's what we're fearing.
We don't want to quash his mechanical bent,
But some things we simply will have to prevent."

His parents agreed with a very deep sigh,
But what could they do with him, what could they try?
Assembling flat pack was one possibility,
But rather than bookshelves he built something military!
They tried him with Airfix kits, paints and some glue,
But Titus preferred building things from the sprue.

Then one day a package was left on the mat.
It looked rather damp, but he didn't mind that.
It bumped and it banged when he shook it about,
Oh what was inside it? He had to find out!
He tore off the paper, the tape and the string,
Ignoring the fact that it wasn't for him.

The soaking wet box didn't take long to open,
A thing to dismantle, and as yet unbroken!
He saw some instructions but threw them away,
The boy was impatient and wanted to play.
He added in bits that he found in his pocket,
And joyfully pushed in the plug at the socket.

Although he was warned, Titus hadn't remembered
Electrical items should not be dismembered,
Or tinkered with when they are patently wet.
But Titus was reckless and prone to forget.
With plumes of white smoke and a blinding white flash,
The boy was reduced to a pile of ash.

UNA EVERSHAM-BLAND

Una Eversham-Bland could often be seen
Walking on pavements while glued to a screen.
Addicted to headphones and smartphone technology,
She bumped into people without an apology.
Completely oblivious to what she had done,
She never stopped typing with finger and thumb.

All warnings to Una were wholly unheeded,
For Una's proclivities could not be impeded.
Onwards she wandered intent on her phone,
Through parks and a busy pedestrian zone.
Hitting a child and a rushing commuter,
Tutting and glaring when people rebuked her.

One day Una wanted to cross a wide street,
Through six lanes of traffic, a foolhardy feat!
She didn't look up at the green traffic light,
And gave some poor drivers a terrible fright.
Quite deaf to the hoots and vehicular shunts,
She made it across without looking up once.

Her mother was worried and often opined,
That youngsters on pavements were far too inclined
To check their new messages, news feed or tweets,
Not just when on paths but when crossing the streets.
She warned of the rapid statistical rise
In accidents causing pedestrians' demise.

But Una just mumbled, as always absorbed
(Despite often looking incredibly bored)
In makeup reviews and cute photos of dogs,
Or selfies with friends and celebrity blogs.
Her mother despaired of her zombie-like child,
Whose phone was a curse that she rightly reviled.

Then one day in June, Una's luck would run out,
Her music so loud she did not hear the shout.
If only she hadn't been quite so engrossed
In writing another ridiculous post!
But Una, not seeing the danger ahead,
Fell into a drain and split open her head.

Since then Una's vision has not been the same,
And using her phone causes terrible pain.
So Una's enrolled on a mindfulness course,
To live in the moment, which many endorse.
In short, she prefers to be part of society,
Not virtual, but real, as it has more variety.

She hasn't abandoned her iPhone of course,
It has far more uses than social discourse.
But Una is no more a slave to her screen;
A much more conversant and happier teen.
She looks where she's going when crossing the street,
And checks every pavement for holes at her feet.

Binko-Nibbs was a boy who liked danger,
He'd do any stunt for a dare or a wager.
Despite all the warnings that everyone gave,
He thought he was dashing and clever and brave.
There weren't many things that the boy wouldn't do,
From shinning up flagpoles to drinking shampoo.

The local police had been called back in June,
When Victor had used an explosive harpoon.
He'd wanted a zip wire for crossing the street,
(James Bond had completed a similar feat).
But luckily someone had seen him take aim,
And phoned the police to protest and complain.

Months later young Victor had wanted to see
The view from the top of the town Christmas tree.
He found some old crampons and borrowed a rope,
And started to climb, well he hadn't a hope!
He clambered his way up the towering spruce,
But fell to the floor when his knots had worked loose.

His injuries sometimes were really appalling,
But Victor was rarely concerned about falling.
Despite all the sprains and the fractures and breaks,
The boy didn't learn from his painful mistakes.
He always had one of his limbs sheathed in plaster.
The doctors called Victor a walking disaster!

Sadly, the child's endless quest for more thrills
Was thwarted by Victor's supreme lack of skills.
For though he was known for his pluck and audacity,
He didn't have patience or much perspicacity
To think through his exploits before he began.
He never prepared or came up with a plan.

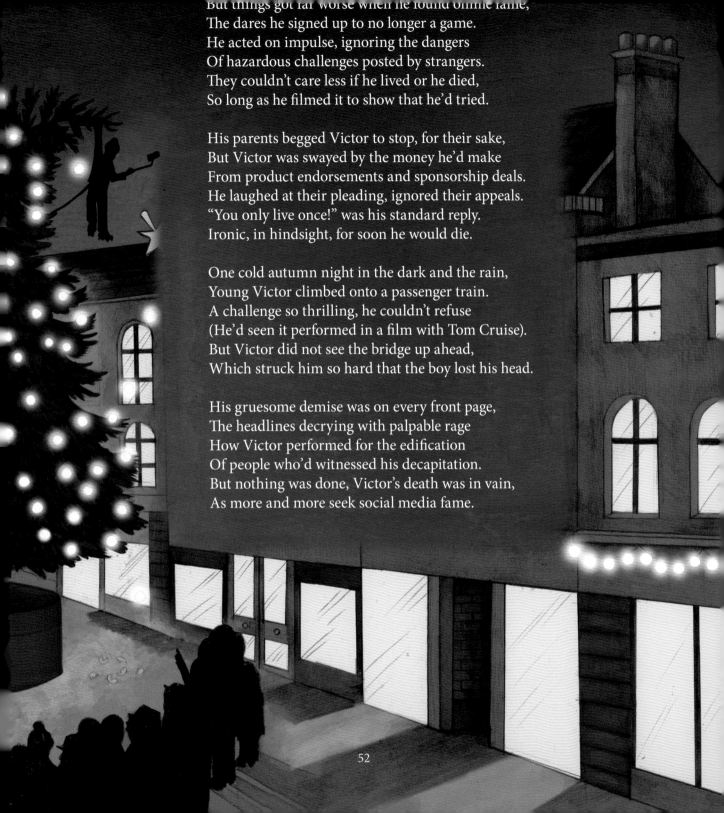

But things got far worse when he found online fame,
The dares he signed up to no longer a game.
He acted on impulse, ignoring the dangers
Of hazardous challenges posted by strangers.
They couldn't care less if he lived or he died,
So long as he filmed it to show that he'd tried.

His parents begged Victor to stop, for their sake,
But Victor was swayed by the money he'd make
From product endorsements and sponsorship deals.
He laughed at their pleading, ignored their appeals.
"You only live once!" was his standard reply.
Ironic, in hindsight, for soon he would die.

One cold autumn night in the dark and the rain,
Young Victor climbed onto a passenger train.
A challenge so thrilling, he couldn't refuse
(He'd seen it performed in a film with Tom Cruise).
But Victor did not see the bridge up ahead,
Which struck him so hard that the boy lost his head.

His gruesome demise was on every front page,
The headlines decrying with palpable rage
How Victor performed for the edification
Of people who'd witnessed his decapitation.
But nothing was done, Victor's death was in vain,
As more and more seek social media fame.

WINNIE YUMMLY-SCOTT

Winnie was raised in the ice and the snow,
Where temperatures often fell thirty below.
A small Greenland village adjacent to Nuuk
(It's not on the map, so don't bother to look).
Her mother was studying permafrost thawing,
A subject that Winnie had always found boring.

"You need to find out," Winnie's mother said brightly,
"What happens when temperatures rise even slightly.
When polar ice melts and the tundra defrosts,
The sea levels rise, meaning lives will be lost.
"And then," she went on, "there's the risk of starvation
For creatures on ice floes which face devastation."

Now Winnie was young, only thirteen years old,
And outside the weather still *seemed* very cold.
Long icicles hung from the eaves of their roof,
Thermometers giving numerical proof
That though it was April the air was still chilly,
To say ice was melting was patently silly!

Cooped up in their cottage with nothing to do,
Poor Winnie would sit in her mother's canoe.
Pretending to paddle across open seas,
Or down melting rivers with consummate ease.
She dreamt about skating on blue polar ice,
Just feeling the wind in her hair would be nice!

One day Winnie's mother prepared to go out,
"Oh please can I come, I can be your lookout."
Said Winnie, who knew of the danger from bears.
"Come on," said her mother, with one of her stares,
"Just listen and do as I say," she implored,
"We're going to somewhere I've not yet explored."

The two of them ventured out into the gloom,
Their path by the shoreline lit up by the moon.
"Stay close," said her mother, "don't go out of sight."
"Don't worry," said Winnie, "we'll both be alright."
She patted the rifle slung over her shoulder,
A sensible measure that made her feel bolder.

An hour or two later they found the location,
With something approaching a sense of elation.
Her mother unloaded her auger and drills,
While Winnie ran round to alleviate chills.
"I'm frozen," she called, "can I go for a skate?"
"Not yet," said her mother, "just stand there and wait."

Impatiently, Winnie decided to leave,
And past jagged glaciers started to weave.
Her skates carving grooves in the ice on the bay,
As further and further she sped on her way.
And then Winnie heard a loud crack to her right;
The ice broke apart and she vanished from sight.

Her mother called out, but her cries were in vain.
No sign of a struggle, no spreading bloodstain,
No polar bears feasting on tasty fresh meat,
And then she caught sight of her poor daughter's feet.
Protruding straight up through a hole in the ice,
Stuck fast, Winnie froze as if held in a vice.

If only poor Winnie had heeded the warning
Her mother had given about global warming,
She might not have ventured on ice that was thin,
But sadly she did, and of course she fell in.
Like many her age, Winnie thought she knew best,
She didn't of course, as we now can attest.

XERXES STAMP*

*Metre change!

At 15 Melchett Avenue resided Xerxes Stamp,
Unwashed and so dishevelled that he could have been a tramp.
The reason for his ill-kempt look and faintly mouldering scent,
Was due to all his rodents and the time with them he spent.
While not forgetting lagomorphs and all those squeaking creatures,
Like voles and gerbils, mice and shrews that share so many features.

His attic room was home to nearly every sort of vermin,
With sawdust, hay, and hamster wheels, and cages for his ermine.
He catered to his furry friends and pandered to their habits,
With burrows under floorboards for his families of rabbits.
Downstairs, his aunt ignored the funny noises she could hear,
She put it down to being drunk on potent home-brewed beer!

But keeping creatures well-renowned for rampant copulation,
Led to overcrowding and a different complication.
A side-effect of keeping a menagerie so large,
Was droppings by the bucket load and urinary discharge,
Which seeped into the plasterwork and caused a nasty stink,
Compounded by the smell of fish he bought to feed his mink.

The ghastly whiff was bad enough, as well as swarms of fleas,
On top of which he ran the risk of getting Weil's disease.
A nasty illness passed to humans in the wee of rats,
Which at its worst can sometimes cause your organs to collapse!
He read up on this ailment to make a diagnosis,
The last thing Xerxes wanted was to catch Leptospirosis!

Then there was the cost involved, which made him rather tense,
For as the population grew, so too did the expense.
Just shopping for the food alone was more than he could manage,
Plus all the bills at hardware shops to rectify the damage.
His aunt was not forthcoming when he asked her for a loan,
The look she gave poor Xerxes could have turned the boy to stone.

A different plan to feed his brood was what he sorely needed,
And just like that, the answer came, the garden could be weeded!
The plot was large and overgrown but had been full of veg,
But first he'd need to fight his way through brambles and a hedge.
With loppers, gloves and secateurs, the boy attacked the boscage,
And there beneath the undergrowth, he found some crops to forage.

He filled his baskets to the brim, he even found a swede!
Plus sorrel leaves and dandelions his guinea pigs would need.
But as he climbed the spiral stairs up to his private zoo,
A shocking smell assailed his nose like slowly burning glue.
He ran into the attic room and saw an awful sight,
A cable had been gnawed right through and set the room alight!

The squeaks and cries were deafening as creatures scampered out,
All swarming past poor Xerxes who had little time to shout.
The angry mink and great big rats all bit and scratched and clawed,
As Xerxes screamed and tried to save the pets he so adored.
He fled the scene and burst outside as fire raged within,
His bottom red with puncture wounds and grazes on his chin.

The RSPCA were called and took the case to court.
They banned the boy from keeping pets and wrote a long report.
His feckless aunt who fled the blaze was also vilified,
Her lack of care and drunkenness were quite unjustified.
So if you love all furry things please practise segregation,
Or run the risk they'll reproduce and cause an infestation.

YORICK STICKLETHWICK

Yorick grew up on a street in Herne Hill,
He longed for adventure and never stayed still.
He vaulted with ease over high garden walls,
And climbed up on rooftops, ignoring the calls
Of neighbours who said he would surely be killed!
But Yorick was doughty and very strong-willed.

When Yorick turned ten he was given a bike,
An old BMX that his dad thought he'd like.
In minutes young Yorick was pedalling hard,
And zooming around in their tiny back yard.
Then off to the park where he flew down the hills,
Jumping and skidding, perfecting his skills.

But Yorick, though gifted, was reckless and bold,
He didn't like helmets and wouldn't be told.
"They make me look stupid and mess up my hair,"
He said to his mother, and gave her a glare.
"I don't want to wear one, it's not like I'm five!"
"Come on," said his mum, "it'll keep you alive."

Yorick refused, though he said he'd behave,
Then picked up his bike and took off with a wave.
Of course he was lying, and once out of sight,
He wheelied down pavements with whoops of delight.
Whenever he could he would try out new tricks,
Like bunny-hops, endos and even back flips.

Quite rightly, his antics were met with aggression,
For Yorick was guilty of every transgression.
By shunning the law and the rules of the road
There wasn't a driver the boy didn't goad.
He undertook buses and never gave way.
The lad was foolhardy, a true tearaway!

But Yorick ignored all the shouts of frustration,
The fist-shaking, hooting, and signs of vexation
From drivers and cyclists who stuck to the rules.
He labelled them slowcoaches, morons and fools!
But one day such arrogance caught the boy out,
When Yorick rode up to a large roundabout.

As usual, he sailed through every red light,
(Which gave people crossing a horrible fright),
Before racing over the double white lines,
And failing to stop at the big Give Way signs.
He ducked through a gap as he pedalled at speed,
Without looking right, what a fatal misdeed!

The witnesses called by the judge to explain,
Had all said the cyclist was clearly to blame.
The lorry that hit him had no time to stop,
And crushed Yorick's skull with a sickening pop.
So drive with respect and adhere to the rules,
Whatever the type of conveyance you use.

ZILLAH GODIVA

Zillah attended a top public school,
With ancient traditions and numerous rules.
They taught girls deportment and ladylike graces,
And Latin on Sundays (yes, one of those places).
In short, it was perfect for those who aspired
To get on in life and be greatly admired.

Zillah had boarded from quite a young age.
Her parents had rapidly got to the stage,
Where Zillah's demands for parental attention
Had caused quite significant marital tension.
Her mother resented the mess and the noise,
And Father was missing his golf with the boys.

So Zillah was packed off to school with a wave.
"Don't cry," they exhorted, "come on now, be brave!"
But things went awry and soon phone calls ensued,
The girl seldom spoke and was often subdued.
Her housemaster told them she still wet the bed,
Perhaps she could be a day pupil instead?

But Mr and Mrs Godiva demurred,
Explaining that Zillah could surely be cured.
"She just needs some time to make friends and join in,
She's much better there," said her dad with a grin.
"And anyway, we're going off on a cruise.
Just don't forget how much in fees you would lose!"

Eventually after some months of distress,
Their daughter no longer seemed quite so depressed.
Indeed, as her teachers were pleased to report,
Young Zillah was coping without their support.
Her parents concluded she'd turned out alright.
But nobody knew what she did late at night!

As soon as her classmates were tucked up in bed,
Young Zillah climbed out of the window instead.
Across the school grounds she made off like a thief,
And reached the school fence which she crawled underneath.
Not too far beyond was a hut in a wood,
And there, sad to say, she got up to no good.

After some time came a knock at the door,
And in came some friends she had met there before.
Their pockets were stuffed full of chocolates and sweets,
While Zillah had crisps and a bagful of treats.
They turned on some music and kicked off their shoes,
Then somebody brought out a bottle of booze...

Zillah was shocked, but could be led astray,
She worried about what her school friends would say.
She'd always been known as a bit of a prude,
And not joining in would have made her seem rude.
So steeling herself, she held out an old cup,
Which to her dismay, was completely filled up.

Zillah downed all of the strong-tasting drink,
Her two so-called friends gave each other a wink.
They topped up her cup and then plied her with more,
Till Zillah turned white and collapsed on the floor.
The poor girl was killed by a litre of gin,
Consumed in the hope it would make her fit in.

The End

GLOSSARY

The Strange Tales of the Alphabet Children is full of words you wouldn't expect to find in a children's book. That may be because this isn't *strictly* a children's book at all, something I hinted at in the preface.

Either way, I strongly believe that far too many children's books these days are 'dumbed down' to make them easy to read. There is a common assumption that children can only manage simple words, or that they will be put off if they find a word they don't know, which I think is rather patronising.

In my experience, children love experimenting with new words. Besides, how else do you expand your vocabulary if you only come across words you already know? Even as an adult, I often need to consult a dictionary, particularly when reading anything written by the incredible Stephen Fry. So I make no apologies for using words like lagomorph* in this book (even though I had to look that one up myself).

However, because I also know that many children (and adults) won't know what a lagomorph is, I decided to write my own glossary. Of course, you may not need it. You may know what a lagomorph is. You may even find the fact that I have provided a glossary to *be* patronising, although I hope you don't.

So without further ado, here it is. Please note that I have not included words used outside the stories, and some words may have more than one meaning, in which case I've given you the meaning relevant to the story they're in. The glossary does not provide perfect dictionary definitions either, so please don't be offended if you happen to be a lexicographer**.

*Lagomorph - an order of mammals to which rabbits belong. They're not rodents, despite having pointy front teeth (as I discovered when writing Xerxes Stamp). So now you know.

**Lexicographer - somebody who writes or compiles a dictionary.

AMY

Contrite
Sorry for something you've done.

Eureka
In Greek, Eureka means 'I have it!'. This is what Archimedes, a Greek scientist, shouted one day in the bath when he discovered how to measure the volume of an irregular shape.

Elevated
High up.

Gossamer
A very delicate, fine and light material.

Levitation
To rise or float in the air (often magically).

Mantra
A chant or a phrase that is repeated. Some religions involve lots of chanting.

Meditation
Staying very calm and silent while trying to empty your mind of thoughts. People do it to feel less stressed and more able to cope with day-to-day life.

Newtonian
Relating to Sir Isaac Newton, the physicist who developed the law of gravity when an apple supposedly fell on his head.

Pliers
A tool to grip or squeeze things.

BASIL

Affliction
Something that causes pain or unhappiness - often linked to a disease or illness.

Discern
To see or recognise something.

Divan
A type of bed, often with a base that contains drawers for storing things.

Eluded
When somebody doesn't 'get' or understand something.

Perplexed
Confused.

Petit Pois
French for 'small peas'.

Resolved
Decided.

Tome
A large and heavy book.

CLARA

Abstemious
To not eat or drink (much).

Astronomic
Often used to describe something that is VERY expensive (or large).

Audible
Able to be heard.

Clean eating
Avoiding processed foods (like crisps or chicken nuggets). Clean eating involves only eating food you make from raw ingredients.

Comestible
Food.

Confit
Something cooked for a long time in oil or fat at a low temperature. It makes meat very tender. I'm not sure about leeks.

Devotee
A fan of something or somebody.

Epicurean
Somebody who really enjoys sensory pleasures (usually relating to food).

Esoteric
Something only understood or appreciated by a specialist.

Gastronomic
Relating to food.

Grimace
Pulling a face, usually when you are in pain or disgusted by something.

Implored
Begged.

Jus
A French word meaning a thin gravy or sauce. The 's' is silent incidentally.

Kelp
A type of edible seaweed.

Michelin Stars
A rating system for the world's best and usually most expensive restaurants.

Mocked
Made fun of.

Privation
A lack of food or things you need to live.

Ragu
An Italian meat-based sauce. Basically what you find in Spaghetti Bolognese or a Lasagne.

Refined
Tasteful, classy, elegant.

Schmooze
A slang word meaning to flatter somebody, often to get something in return.

Snide
Making fun of somebody, being nasty.

Sublime
Absolutely amazing or beautiful.

Susceptible
Likely to be affected by something or somebody. If you are susceptible to hayfever for example, you are likely to get it.

Tedious
Boring or dull.

DESMOND

Compounded
Made worse.

Confounded
Surprised when something unexpected happens.

Discharged
Let out.

Eminent
Respected or known for being skilled or clever.

Exhortations
Something that is said to encourage a person to do something.

Floundering
Struggling clumsily.

Midwife
Somebody who helps a woman to have a baby.

Mogul
A rounded snowy bump on a ski run. It's very difficult to ski or snowboard over them without falling over!

Nursery slope
A very gentle hill for beginners to practise skiing or snowboarding.

Piste
A ski run that has been 'groomed' (made flat and even) by a big machine.

Portent
A warning that something bad is about to happen.

Prehensile
Able to grasp something.

Prostration
Lying flat.

Strife
Trouble or difficulty (often involving disagreement).

Trait
A characteristic or common behaviour.

Umbilical Cord
The fleshy cord that joins a baby to its mother. It is cut when the baby is born.

ERNEST

Calories
Energy from food and drink.

Comestibles
Things you can eat.

Consumption
The process of eating and drinking.

Gluttonous
Greedy.

Gorging
Eating very greedily.

Maladies
Illnesses or diseases.

Maw
The mouth or jaws of an animal.

Obese
Fat.

Oesophagus
The tube that connects your throat to your stomach.

Thyroid
A gland in your neck that produces chemicals which affect your heart rate and temperature (amongst other things). People with an 'overactive thyroid' produce lots of these chemicals, meaning they use energy more quickly (which, like Ernest, means they stay hungry despite eating a lot).

FANNY

Ablute
To wash yourself.

Clone
An identical copy.

Conflicting
Being opposed to something.

Constricting
Uncomfortably tight.

Convention
Behaving in a way that most people consider normal.

Decried
Publicly criticised.

Diabetes
A disease that can lead to too much or too little blood sugar.

Eaves
The area under the edges of a roof.

Lulled
Made to feel calm and sleepy.

Poultice
A paste made from natural ingredients thought to have healing properties, which is held against a painful or swollen area using bandages or cloth.

Prescribed
To be recommended or advised.

Profligate

Extravagant, usually describes somebody who spends a lot of money.

Serenade

Sweet, restful singing or music.

Sprite

An elf or fairy.

Tetanus

A disease often caused when a wound or bite gets infected with tetanus bacteria. Not long ago, lots of people died from tetanus, but today, most people are vaccinated and don't catch it.

Unorthodox

Uncommon or unusual.

Untethered

Free. Literally means 'not tied up'.

Validation

Saying that something is OK or acceptable.

GEORGE

Abstain

To stop doing something.

Antisocial

Preferring to be alone.

Attuned

Highly aware of something.

Complex

A mental or emotional problem (rather than the normal definition which means 'complicated').

Desist

Stop.

Dissembling

Trying to hide your true feelings.

Eminent

Respected or known for being skilled or clever.

Evade

Dodge or avoid.

Fetish

A strong liking for something.

Freud (person)

Sigmund Freud was a German doctor who came up with a lot of theories about why people behave in certain ways. He also did a lot of work to explain what dreams mean.

Juvenile

A young person.

Midst

In the middle of.

Nocturnal

An animal that wakes up at night and sleeps during the day.

Shrinks

A slang word for psychiatrists (people who try to understand how peoples' minds work and why people behave in certain ways).

Solstice

When the sun reaches its highest point in the sky (the summer solstice marks the longest day) or its lowest point (the winter solstice marks the shortest day).

Suffocation

Not being able to breathe (and usually dying as a result).

Whittle

To worry about something all the time.

HECTOR

Abhorred

Disliked or hated.

Audacious

Rude and disrespectful. Can also mean bold or willing to take risks (see Victor).

Belligerence

Aggression, anger.

Broadside

A full on attack. In sea battles, it describes a situation where a sailing galleon would present its 'broadside' towards another, enabling it to fire all its cannons to try and sink the other ship.

Carbon Footprint

The amount of carbon dioxide you release into the atmosphere from things you use which are made by burning fossil fuels (petrol, oil, gas etc).

Chastised

Told off.

Demagogue

Somebody who makes people angry or worked up by what they say. Some politicians are very good at doing this - Adolf Hitler was a good example of a demagogue.

Deplored

Thinking something is morally wrong.

Despised

Having a very low opinion of somebody or something.

Facile

Not serious (sometimes used to mean lacking in character).

Gustation

The act of tasting something.

Invincible

Unbeatable.

Loquacious

Very talkative or chatty.

Miscreants
People who have done something wrong or broken the law.

Obnoxious
Very unpleasant or rude.

Oratory
Public speaking.

Sagely
Wisely.

Tirade
A long, angry speech.

Trolls
Now commonly used to mean people who abuse others online.

IDA

Arduous
Difficult, tiring.

Banished
Got rid of.

Birketts
541 hills in the Lake District which are over 1,000 feet in height, as defined in a book by Bill Birkett.

Craved
Desperately wanted.

Dispelled
Got rid of (similar to banished).

Emitting
Giving out.

Humility
Being modest and not boastful.

Ingot
A block of metal.

Mocked
Made fun of.

Nuttalls
445 hills in England and Wales that are over 2,000 feet in height with at least 50 feet of ascent on

all sides. These were defined in a book by John and Anne Nuttall.

Reserve
Keeping your feelings hidden.

Squall
Sudden, strong wind, often with rain.

Spectators
People who watch a live event (often sport).

Tarry
To dawdle or hang around.

Wainwrights
214 English mountains and hills listed in Alfred Wainwright's series of books, 'The Pictorial Guide to the Lakeland Fells.'

JAMES

Adeptness
Skill.

Boycotting
Deliberately not taking part.

Compounds
A substance that contains two or more chemical elements.

Concocting
Making, inventing.

Defiance
A refusal to do something.

Dubious
Not completely honest, a bit dodgy.

Dreary
Dull, boring.

Expulsion
Being thrown out (of school).

Fission
Splitting an atom to create nuclear energy.

Ill-founded
Not thought through properly.

Infraction
A breaking of the rules.

Innovation
An invention or improvement to a design.

Lamentation
Showing that you are sad or upset.

Libation
A drink.

Liberated
Released from.

Lye
A strong alkali chemical (the opposite of an acid) used for cleaning or washing. Not so very different to strong bleach.

MI5
The United Kingdom's internal security service. MI6 is our international security service (where James Bond works!)

Noxious
Poisonous or dangerously unpleasant.

Orbital
Going round something (in this case, going round the Earth).

Plutonium
A chemical element used to make nuclear power.

Propulsion
The means of powering a vehicle, like an engine on a car or sails on a boat.

Quadratics
A complicated mathematical formula that I don't really understand.

Stockpile
Something you have collected a lot of to use later.

Transaction
The act of giving and receiving or buying and selling something.

TNT
An explosive chemical compound. TNT is short for Trinitrotoluene.

Unrefined
Not the pure form of something.

Vowed
Promised.

KATE

Aberration
Something that is unusual or unexpected.

Ascertain
To find out.

Cocooned
Wrapped up.

Conferred
Discussed, often confidentially.

Feat
An act that requires courage or strength.

Frank
Blunt honesty.

Mandarin
A Chinese language.

Paralysis
Being unable to move.

Raiments
A very old word for clothes.

Repertoire
Things you can perform, for example, songs, dances or poems.

Rehabilitation
Getting back to normal, often applied to people getting well after an illness or accident.

Spinal Cord
The thick cord of nerves that connects your brain to the different parts of your body. People are often paralysed when they damage their spinal cord.

Traction
Medical equipment that is used to gently pull a broken leg or arm straight to make sure it heals properly.

X-Rays, CTs, MRIs
Different types of scans you have in hospital that allow doctors to see what's going on inside you. X-Rays mostly look at bones and tumours, CT scans are a detailed type of x-ray that look at bones, blood vessels, organs and soft parts of the body, while MRIs use strong magnets to look in detail at all sorts of different internal body parts.

LEO

Aghast
Shocked and surprised.

Antics
Silly behaviour.

Asinine
Idiotic or stupid.

Chaucer, Keats, Joyce
Three famous authors / poets who you will probably study at school one day, if you haven't already.

Commotion
A lot of confusion and loud excitement.

Escapade
An exciting or dangerous adventure.

Expiration
When something (or somebody) comes to an end.

Goad
To taunt or provoke.

Implications
Something that is likely to happen as a result of something else.

Incite
Persuade or encourage.

Invariably
More often than not, usually.

Misdemeanour
A crime or bad act.

Naught
An old word for nothing.

Oesophagus
The tube that joins your throat to your stomach.

Ratify
To confirm that you agree with something.

Reprimanded
Told off.

Woeful
Bad, or often used to mean 'not very good', for example: 'her performance on the tennis court was woeful.'

MAUD

Abhorred
Disliked intensely.

Blood-curdling
Used to describe the sound you make when you are very frightened - literally means to make your blood thicken and stop flowing.

Bluff
'Call your bluff' is when you

challenge somebody to prove that what they've said or done is true.

Carving
Turning quickly across a wave on a surfboard.

Davy Jones
There are lots of stories about Davy Jones. Most say that he is the sailors' devil, or the ghost of a drowned sailor or pirate. Davy Jones' Locker means the seabed, which is where drowned sailors can end up.

Enthralled
Absolutely fascinated by something.

Exalted
Thought very highly of.

Goliath
From the biblical story, David and Goliath (where Goliath was a giant). Used to mean somebody very large and strong.

Inept
Lacking in skill or bad at doing something.

Riptide
A part of the ocean where two strong currents meet, making it particularly dangerous for swimmers.

NEVILLE

Affliction
Illness.

Agoraphobic
The fear of being outside or in public places.

Apathy
Uninterested or unenthusiastic.

Atrophy
To become weak or waste away.

Baffled
To be unable to explain or understand something.

Balmy
Warm and pleasant.

Boules
A French game where you throw heavy metal balls towards a small white ball called a jack. The closest ball to the jack wins.

Contempt
Having no respect for somebody or something, or thinking they / it are worthless.

Deride
To make fun of.

Enlightening
When you have been given knowledge to help you understand or appreciate something.

Epitomised
Being the perfect example of something.

Feigned
Pretended.

Inconsequential
Of little value or worth.

Inertia
Not moving.

Malaise
When you feel unhappy or depressed.

Maunder
To wander about aimlessly.

Obstinate
Stubborn.

Professed
To declare or say something.

Regimen
A routine.

Squandered
Wasted.

Tenacious
To keep trying without giving up.

Uninspired
Something that is unexciting or dull.

Vexatious
Annoying, something that makes a person angry.

OLIVE

Alchemy
Attempting to turn non-precious metals into gold.

Awl
A pointed tool used to punch holes in leather.

Brandishing
Holding in a threatening way.

Dowels
Thin wooden sticks about the width of a pencil.

Duress
Being pressured to do something.

Excel
To do extremely well or perform at a very high standard.

Fiendish
Cruel or unpleasant.

Imposition
Something imposed, like a punishment or unfair requirement to do something.

Incantation
A magic spell.

Invariably
Usually.

Jotter
Note book.

Mandrake Root

Mandrake roots look (a bit) like people, and if you eat them, you will hallucinate, which means seeing, feeling or hearing weird things that aren't there. They do <u>not</u> cure people who have been 'petrified', as you might gather from Harry Potter.

Nom de Plume

A name used by authors instead of their real name (if they don't want people to know who has written the book).

Noxious

Poisonous or dangerously unpleasant.

Obsessed

Completely focused on.

Parried

Blocked an attack.

Quidditch

The main school sport in the Harry Potter series by J.K. Rowling, played by two teams on broomsticks. I would definitely play Quidditch if I could.

Railed

Criticised something loudly and angrily.

Repository

A place to keep or store things safely.

Straddling

With legs on both sides.

Telepathy

The ability to read somebody else's mind or communicate by thought alone.

Tenon Saw

A small, fine-toothed, rigid saw.

Unbeknownst

An old way of saying 'unknown to'.

PRUE

Armani

An Italian fashion brand named after its founder, Georgio Armani.

Concussed

Feeling sick, confused or even being unconscious after a bang to the head.

Disdain

Disliking something, especially something that you think is unimportant or beneath you.

Ensued

Began, followed on from.

Extravagant

Spending more than you can afford or need to spend.

Flaunting

Showing off.

Haughty

Looking down your nose at somebody, thinking you are better than them.

Immoderate

Unreasonable, excessive.

Inculcation

To make somebody believe or do something by constantly repeating it.

Largesse

Generosity.

Manolo

Manolo Blahnik - a Spanish ladies' shoe maker who makes unbelievably expensive shoes.

Ordeal

A situation that is difficult or unpleasant.

Peers

People roughly the same age as you.

Predilection

A particular liking for something.

Scam

A trick to con somebody out of money.

Sham

Something that isn't real or isn't what it seems to be.

Tiffany

A company that sells very expensive jewellery.

Trait

Characteristic.

Transitory

Not lasting long, temporary.

Unremitting

Happening constantly without a break or pause.

Unwitting

Without knowing.

Vain

A person who cares too much about how they look.

QUENTIN

Attentively

Paying close attention.

Dedication

Being committed. What you need, for example, if you want to learn a musical instrument, do well at school or play a sport really well.

Entreaties
Polite but serious requests to do something.

Gore
Blood from a wound.

Gruelling
Very hard and physically tiring.

Impeded
Prevented or stopped.

Manic
Extremely busy.

Mire
Deep mud, dirt or marshland.

Ordeal
A situation that is difficult or unpleasant.

Onerous
Another word for something that is difficult or unpleasant.

Perspire
Sweat.

Slurry
Solids mixed with water to form a goopy liquid, in this case used to describe big tanks of liquid animal poo. Ugh.

Smallholding
A small farm.

Suffocation
Not being able to breathe, usually resulting in death.

Walling
Making dry stone walls - which is much harder than it sounds!

RHODA

Affliction
Something that causes pain or unhappiness - often linked to a disease or illness.

Allay
Reduce or stop.

Cairngorms
A mountain range in the eastern Highlands of Scotland.

Composure
Being calm.

Conviction
Strong belief.

Cremated
Burned, the alternative to being buried when you die.

Disembarked
Got off - usually a bus, boat, train or plane.

Fretted
Worried.

Geologists
People who study the Earth's structure and its rocks and minerals.

Heeded
Listened to, accepted as fact.

Histrionics
Dramatic or exaggerated behaviour. When somebody overreacts.

Hydrogen Sulphide
A poisonous, flammable gas that smells really, really bad. People say it smells of rotten eggs, though I've never actually smelled rotten eggs. If you ever smell a 'stink bomb', that is what they are filled with. I think.

Implored
Begged.

Magma
Rock that is heated until turns into a liquid. What you see flowing out of a volcano.

Nonplussed
Confused or unsure.

Phobia
A strong fear.

Pockmarked
Dented and pitted, like the moon.

Pyroclastic
Rocks formed from the lava and bits of rock that get blown out of a volcano.

Relent
To allow something to happen that you didn't allow before. If you've been banned from playing computer games by your mum for example, she might relent if you are really, really good and say sorry a lot.

Seismic
Relating to earthquakes.

Tectonics
Relating to the Earth's crust.

Truncated
Cut short.

Vent
A hole allowing gas to escape.

Volcanologists
People who study volcanoes.

SUSAN

Ailments
Illnesses.

Blue Murder
To shout 'blue murder' means to scream or shout very loudly. It comes from the French, 'Mort Bleu' or blue death.

Bunkum
Nonsense.

Defiance
Refusing to do something.

Eliminate
Get rid of.

Harrowing
Very upsetting or disturbing.

Pique
Annoyance.

Seizure
A sudden, violent attack (of an illness).

Transgress
To break the rules.

Trauma
A very upsetting event or major shock.

Vexation
Annoyance.

TITUS

Airfix Kits
Plastic scale models made by a company called Airfix that you build from moulded plastic parts and paint yourself. I made loads of them as a boy, but always managed to get glue everywhere. My brother Tim was much more careful...

Bent
A natural interest or ability.

Confided
To have told somebody a secret.

Dismember
To pull apart.

Gladiator
A person in Roman times who was forced to fight other people or wild animals in front of an audience. There was a lot of blood and somebody usually got killed. Not surprisingly.

Ingot
A block of metal.

Obsession
Something (or somebody) a person thinks about all the time until it gets a bit weird.

Patently
Obviously.

Plumes
Large clouds.

Prone
Tending to. You might be prone to stomach aches or prone to getting colds. Similar to 'susceptible' (see Clara).

Quash
Discourage, prevent.

Repurpose
Turn something into something else or give it a new use.

Sprue
The plastic frame that holds all the pieces in an Airfix kit together. You'll understand when you see one. I used to melt sprue over a candle flame to make aerials for my models.

Tinkered
To fiddle about with, or make small improvements to something. People often 'tinker' with their cars to make them look or drive better. I tinker a lot.

Unwittingly
Without realising.

UNA

Conversant
Familiar with.

Demise
Death or end.

Discourse
Conversation.

Endorse
Give your approval to something or somebody.

Engrossed
Completely absorbed by or focussed on something.

Enrolled
Signed up for, joined.

Foolhardy
Taking unnecessary or foolish risks.

Impeded
Prevented or stopped from doing something.

Mindfulness
Being aware of your surroundings 'in the moment' by using all your senses. Not thinking about the past or the future, just being.

Oblivious
Unaware of.

Opined
Gave an opinion about something.

Proclivities
Things you are very interested in or tend to do.

Rebuked
Told off.

Reviled
Angrily criticised.

Unheeded
Not listened to, ignored.

Vehicular
To do with vehicles.

VICTOR

Audacity
Daring, risk-taking.

Clambered
Climbed with hands and feet.

Crampons

Spiked metal frames you can fit to the sole of walking boots to climb safely on snow and ice.

Dashing

Handsome and stylish.

Decapitation

When your head is chopped off.

Decrying

Criticising.

Demise

Death, the end.

Edification

Education or improvement.

Exploits

Feats of daring or bravery.

Feat

Something you do that takes courage or a lot of effort or skill.

Hindsight

Literally means 'looking back'. The phrase 'with the benefit of hindsight' is used when you might have done something differently, if only you had known what would have happened when you did it.

Impulse

Doing something in the heat of the moment without thinking.

Ironic

The opposite of what you would expect to happen (sort of).

Palpable

Something real, easy to see.

Perspicacity

The ability to think or understand something clearly.

Pluck

Bravery.

Product Endorsements

Saying in public that you like a product or thing. People on social media with lots of followers are often paid to endorse a particular product so that it sells more.

Sponsorship Deals

Being paid to promote, advertise or do something. Famous people are often sponsored by big brands to wear their clothes or watches for example. This is also a type of product endorsement (see earlier).

Wager

A bet.

WINNIE

Alleviate

To reduce or make less.

Auger

A large type of drill for boring holes in the ground or in ice.

Attest

Show to be true.

Consummate

Skilful.

Elation

Extreme happiness or excitement.

Heeded

Listened to, paid attention to.

Ice Floes

Sheets of floating ice.

Implored

Begged.

Numerical

To do with numbers.

Patently

Obviously.

Permafrost

Land that is permanently frozen to a great depth. Unfortunately, global warming means that a lot of the permafrost is melting.

Protruding

Sticking out.

Tundra

Vast areas of land in northern America, Asia and Europe where the land is permanently frozen (although not so much these days!)

Vice

A heavy metal tool that clamps things together.

XERXES

Ailment

Illness.

Assailed

Violently attacked.

Boscage

Thickly planted shrubs and plants.

Brood

Babies, children.

Copulation

The act of making babies.

Diagnosis

Working out what's wrong with somebody who is ill.

Dishevelled

Untidy.

Ermine

A stoat with a white winter coat.

Feckless

Irresponsible or careless.

Forage

Search for food.

Forthcoming

Coming up, about to happen.

Ill-kempt

Like dishevelled - untidy.

Infestation
Overrun, often by pests like fleas, mice or rats.

Lagomorph
The order of animals which rabbits belong to. As I discovered, rabbits are NOT rodents, despite having sticky-outy teeth and fur.

Leptospirosis
Another name for Weil's Disease (see later).

Loppers
A sharp, long-handled tool for cutting branches.

Menagerie
A collection of wild animals.

Mink
A furry animal like a stoat with slightly webbed feet. Mink are good swimmers and vicious predators. They used to be bred in mink farms for their warm, thick fur, which was turned into luxurious coats. Fortunately, breeding and killing mink doesn't happen much any more and people rarely wear animal fur because it is considered cruel and unnecessary (unless you happen to live in very cold countries where animal skins and fur is used to keep warm).

Mouldering
Slowly rotting.

Pandered
To have done everything that somebody wanted.

Potent
Powerful, strong.

Rampant
Increasing in an uncontrolled way.

Rectify
Fix or make good.

Resided
Lived.

Secateurs
A sharp hand tool gardeners use to cut thin twigs and branches.

Segregation
Being kept apart.

Urinary
To do with urine or wee.

Vilified
When somebody has said horrible things about you.

Weil's Disease
A nasty disease you can catch from the wee of vermin (like mice and rats).

YORICK

Adhere
Follow or stick to, usually in connection to rules or laws.

Aggression
Angry, threatening behaviour.

Antics
Silly behaviour.

Arrogance
Self-importance. In Yorick's case, thinking he was above the law and could do what he liked.

Conveyance
A type of transport or vehicle.

Doughty
Brave, determined.

Endo
When riding a bike, applying the front brake to stop so that your back wheel comes up in the air. Just make sure you don't flip over the handlebars if you do it.

Foolhardy
Taking unnecessary or foolish risks.

Goad
To tease or taunt.

Misdeed
What you do when you break a rule or do something bad.

Morons
Idiots, fools.

Shunning
Ignoring.

Tearaway
A young person who is always in trouble.

Transgression
A breaking of the rules or laws.

Vexation
Annoyance, frustration.

ZILLAH

Aspired
Wanted to become something.

Awry
Gone wrong.

Booze
A slang word for alcohol.

Consumed
Eaten or drunk.

Deportment
How you behave, walk or stand. If you have ever been told not to slouch, or to stand up straight, your deportment was being criticised!

Demurred
To object to something, or be reluctant to do it.

Dismay
A strong feeling of worry or sadness.

Exhorted

Encouraged or persuaded to do something.

Marital tension

When a married couple argue and get stressed.

Numerous

Many.

Plied

To repeatedly try to give somebody something, usually food or drink.

Prude

A person who is shocked or easily embarrassed.

Steeling

To prepare for something unpleasant.

Subdued

Quiet, withdrawn.

ABOUT THE AUTHOR

I was born in 1973, and grew up in Gretton, a smallish village in north Northamptonshire. As the youngest of four by a sizeable margin, I was generally left to my own devices. From memory, I spent most of my time roaming the countryside, playing computer games or making Airfix kits.

After the usual treadmill of school, exams and university, I moved to London to train as a solicitor; a career that I thought I might enjoy, but ended up mostly hating. Parting company with the legal profession a few years after qualifying (a blessed release both for me and the legal profession), I side-stepped into management consultancy and eventually gravitated towards internal communication. I set up my own consultancy in 2009, which still keeps me busy today.

I moved to Rutland with my wife Saskia and two cats in 2011, having become increasingly intolerant of people and noise. Since then, I have acquired two children and lost both a cat and quite a lot of hair. My current claim to fame is that I recently appeared on Gardeners' World and heard Monty Don speak my name. The fact that this should excite me points towards my advancing years.

When not building things for my children or repairing our crumbling home, I spend my remaining free time writing, hillwalking, taking photographs or generally 'tinkering' in my study. This latter activity seems to occupy an increasingly large part of my leisure time. I also have an unhealthy fixation with fancy dress, which I blame on my parents (who both loved amateur dramatics).

Getting a great night's sleep continues to be one of my main life goals.

THANK YOU

With the luxury of blank pages to fill, I'd like to thank all the people who have made this book possible.

Cath Bolton and Nan McClymont, thank you for being such inspirational English teachers during my time at Lodge Park. Your humour, insight and dedication in the classroom all those years ago helped shape my writing style and love of English. Those were truly formative years.

Scrolling forwards, thanks to Julia at Scandimania in Uppingham and the team at Fika in Oakham (Jo, Tia and Laura) for providing a much-needed bolt-hole while *The Strange Tales of the Alphabet Children* was taking shape. You sustained me throughout with excellent coffee, cakes, lunches and (at Fika) fabulously ribald banter!

Thanks to Saint Lewis, Keith Hensby and Gary Andrews for your artistic skill and generosity. Your wonderful illustrations and belief in *The Strange Tales of the Alphabet Children* showed how my stories could be brought to life, and was a huge boost when I needed it most. Thanks to the talented Deborah Panesar, who ultimately took on the role of illustrator and stuck with it right up to the birth of her son. How you produced so many illustrations so quickly is a miracle. It's been a pleasure working with you.

Thanks to my old school friend Lesley Carley for your support, encouragement and early proof-reading. 'Tally-ho, yippety-dap and zing zang spillip' to Richard Wayman for services above and beyond the call of duty. Apart from being an absolutely splendid chap, your intellect, insight and eagle eye for spelling mistakes, grammatical faux pas and plot holes have made you quite the best editor I could have wished for. This book has become immeasurably stronger as a result of your careful ministrations!

Finally, thanks to Saskia and my family, friends and the numerous people on Facebook and beyond who have provided so much biased praise, friendly feedback and general positivity since the project started. Even if this book remains essentially a vanity 'bucket list' project, it's been great fun to write and all the more worthwhile with so many of you behind me.

BEHIND THE SCENES...

First draft in progress, Scandimania, Uppingham 2017.

Working on the preface, Fika, Oakham 2018.

DIY sound recording booth for audiobook recordings.

Early advertising in the COVID-19 lockdown.

First proof arrives...

Basil Bennett, sample illustration by Gary Andrews.

Basil Bennett, sample illustration by Keith Hensby.

Basil Bennett, final spread by Deborah Panesar.

Amy Fettlesham-Flynn, sample illustration by Saint Lewis

Alternative cover colour scheme, by Deborah Panesar.